Jack and The Beanstalk
Beanstalk
Colouring & Storybook

Published by
GRANDREAMS LIMITED
Jadwin House, 205/211 Kentish Town Road,
London, NW5 2JU.

Printed in Hungary

FT15-20

Once upon a time there was a boy named Jack who lived with his mother in a tiny cottage in the country. One day when Jack sat down for dinner, his mother opened the cupboard and found there was no food left.

They had nothing left but their cow, Clara. So his mother said: "Tomorrow, Jack, you must take Clara to market and sell her. She is a good cow and we are sure to get a good price for her."

Next morning Jack got up early, said goodbye to his mother, told her not to worry and set off to market.

He had only gone a little way when he met a man coming up the hill. "I will exchange these magic beans for your cow," said the man and he showed Jack some strange looking coloured beans.

Jack thought how wonderful it would be to have some magic beans and he handed over the cow. Then he ran home, thinking how pleased his mother would be at such a bargain.

But Jack's mother
was very cross and threw
the beans out of the
window and sent Jack
straight to bed. "Oh
dear, and I thought the
magic beans were a real
bargain," Jack kept
telling himself.

When Jack woke up the next morning he thought how dark it was. Then, when he went across to his window, he found that he could hardly see out - for a huge tree had sprung up overnight.

Jack hurried outside and discovered that it wasn't a tree in the garden, but a huge green beanstalk that had grown from the magic beans. He started to climb it.

The beanstalk was so
high that Jack could not
see the top. Up and up
he went, higher and
higher till the ground
below disappeared from
view.

When at last Jack reached the top, he found himself on a long white road leading to a huge castle. It was so big that Jack could only stop and stare.

Jack set off along the road and met an old woman who knew his name. "Jack," she said, "you are in a country belonging to a wicked giant. When you were a baby he stole your mother's belongings."

"That is why your mother is so poor," the old woman continued. "You must try to get back your mother's wealth."

"I shall try," promised Jack, as the woman disappeared in a cloud of smoke and coloured stars.

When Jack reached the castle and knocked on the door, it was opened by the biggest woman that he had ever seen.

"I am tired and hungry," said Jack politely. "Can you give me supper and a night's lodging?"

"Oh, my poor boy," said the woman. "My husband is a giant and he eats people - he might eat you for supper!" But Jack pleaded with her so she sat him down and gave him something to eat.

Soon he was enjoying a hearty meal, but before he had finished there came the thump, thump, thump of heavy feet. "My husband has returned," whispered the woman. "Quick, hide in the old oven."

The giant walked in sniffing the air. "Fe-Fi-Fo-Fum! I smell the blood of an Englishman! Be he alive or be he dead, I'll grind his bones to make my bread!" he thundered.

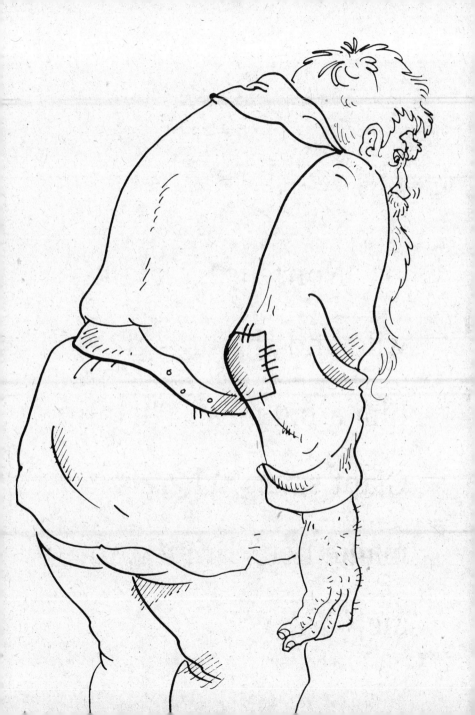

"Nonsense," said his wife and she brought him a big meal. Then the Giant said: "Where's my magic hen? Bring it to me!"

The hen was placed on the table. "Lay!" shouted the Giant and the hen laid a golden egg. "Another!" ordered the Giant over and over again until twelve golden eggs were laid.

As soon as the Giant
had fallen asleep, which
he always did after his
supper, Jack nipped out
of the oven, picked up
the hen and tiptoed
away.

Jack ran and ran until he reached the beanstalk, then he quickly climbed down it back to the cottage.

"Look mother," Jack cried. "This is a magic hen and she lays eggs of pure gold. We can sell them for money to buy food."

However, Jack remembered what the old woman had told him about the Giant stealing his mother's belongings and soon he set off up the beanstalk again.

This time he did not knock at the door but he saw a window open high in the tower. 'I'll climb up there,' thought Jack, 'and get in that way.'

When Jack looked through the window, he saw the giant place his magic harp on the table. "Sing to me," roared the Giant. "I like music after dinner."

Jack waited until the Giant fell asleep. Then he picked up the harp, but as he made off with it, the harp cried: "Master! Master!" and woke the Giant.

At this, Jack ran as fast as his legs would carry him. He could hear the Giant pounding after him and getting nearer and nearer.

Jack reached the top of the beanstalk and scrambled down as fast as he could clutching the magic harp.

He saw his mother below and called out: "Mother! Mother! Bring me the axe!" As he reached the ground his mother ran towards him holding the axe.

There was no time to lose, for the Giant was half-way down. With one mighty blow Jack swung the axe and chopped down the beanstalk.

"Just in time," cried Jack, as the beanstalk, with the Giant clinging to it, crashed to the ground. The ground opened up and swallowed the Giant. He was never seen again.

Then the woman who first met Jack appeared and told him she was a Fairy and led him to the Giant's castle. "Your troubles are over," she said. "You will both be very happy as long as you live." And they were, too.

The End